# CARL MARIA VON WEBER

# CONCERTO

for Bassoon and Orchestra
für Fagott und Orchester
F major / F-Dur / Fa majeur
op. 75
(J 127)

## Ernst Eulenburg Ltd

London · Mainz · Madrid · New York · Paris · Tokyo · Toronto · Zürich

# Weber, Bassoon Concerto, F major, op. 75

Weber's claim to immortality rests mainly on his operatic works and especially on their overtures. It would, however, be wrong to underestimate for this reason his output in the field of vocal and, above all, instrumental music. It is true that in these works he did not go markedly new ways, but nevertheless he enriched the then existing literature to a large degree. Following the example of Mozart, he brought to the fore the wind instruments (which, until then, had occupied a subordinate place) and at the same time exploited the technical possibilities of every one to the fullest extent. In the year 1805 he began with the Romanza Siciliana for Flute, which was followed by a Concertino for Horn. The climax of this creative period was 1811, which Weber spent in Munich. This year was marked by his friendship with the leading clarinettist of that time, C. H. Baermann, for whom he wrote a number of works, partly at the instigation of King Max Josef of Bavaria. Amongst them were two concertos, of which already the first one was so successful, that the bassoon-player G. H. Brandt (like Baermann a member of the Münchner Hofkapelle) was induced to commission a similar work for his instrument. Weber, then 25, was only too willing to accede to this request. In its general outline the concerto was similar to those for clarinet : A march-like first movement is followed by an effective *cantilena* and a *rondo* full of humour. For the dates of this concerto we have to rely on Weber's diary entries. Accordingly we only know that it was completed on 27th November 1811, but nothing is noted about the first performance. The only other mention is

# Weber, Fagott - Konzert, F dur, op. 75

Weber verdankt zwar die Unsterblichkeit seines Namens in erster Linie seinen Bühnenwerken und vor allem den dazu geschriebenen Ouverturen ; aber es wäre ganz falsch, darüber seine Leistungen in der Vokal- und vor allem in der Instrumentalmusik zu unterschätzen. Wenn er auch auf diesen Gebieten kein ausgesprochener Bahnbrecher war, hat er doch die damals vorhandene Literatur gewaltig bereichert und hat vor allem, das Vorbild Mozarts nachahmend, die Stellung der Blasinstrumente, die bis dahin einen untergeordneten Rang eingenommen hatten, gehoben und dabei die technischen und Spielmöglichkeiten eines jeden dieser Instrumente voll ausgeschöpft. So begann er 1805 mit der Romanza Siciliana für Flöte, der ein Concertino für Horn folgte. Den Höhepunkt dieser Schaffensperiode bildete das Jahr 1811, das er in München verbrachte. Er war dort mit dem führenden Klarinettisten der Zeit, C. H. Baermann befreundet und schrieb für diesen, zum Teil auf Anregung des Königs Max Josef von Bayern, eine ganze Anzahl Werke, darunter 2 Konzerte, von denen schon das erste einen so durchschlagenden Erfolg hatte, dass der Fagottist G. H. Brandt, ebenso wie Baermann Mitglied der Münchener Hofkapelle, dadurch angetrieben wurde, sich von Weber ein gleiches Werk für sein Instrument zu bestellen. das der damals 25 jährige auch bereitwillig schrieb. Es war in der Anlage ganz ähnlich denen für Klarinette und besteht aus einem marschartigen 1. Satz, einer dankbaren *Kantilene* und einem *Rondo* voll echtem Witz. Für die Daten dieses Konzerts sind wir auf Webers Tagebuch-Notizen angewiesen. Wi.

a later performance in Prague, also by Brandt, on 19th February 1813.

As was the case with the Concertino for Horn, Weber revised this concerto ten years after its composition. On 17th October 1822, after he had meanwhile become famous, he finally gave it to the publisher Schlesinger in Berlin, who, as was the custom of the time, only printed the parts. Nor was a score issued at a later date, so that this present edition is the first printed score of the Bassoon Concerto.

The opus number 75 was accorded to the work at its first impression ; Weber himself numbers it as no. 74.

Max Alberti.

wissen danach nur, dass es am 27. November 1811 beendet, dagegen nicht, wann es zuerst aufgeführt wurde. Erwähnt wird nur eine spätere Aufführung am 19. Februar 1813 in Prag, ebenfalls durch Brandt.

Genau wie das Concertino für Horn hat Weber auch dieses Konzert etwa 10 Jahre nach der Komposition umgearbeitet und es erst am 17. Oktober 1822, nachdem er inzwischen berühmt geworden war, dem Verlag Schlesinger in Berlin übergeben, der, wie damals üblich, nûr die Stimmen druckte, und es auch später unterliess, eine Partitur folgen zu lassen, sodass die hier vorgelegte Ausgabe tatsächlich die erste gedruckte Partitur dieses schönen Werkes ist.

Die Opus-Zahl 75 wurde beim Druck festgesetzt ; Webers eigenes Verzeichnis giebt 74 an.

Max Alberti.

# CONCERTO

C. M. V. Weber, op. 75
1786-1826

## I

Allegro ma non troppo

2 Flauti — 2 Oboi — 2 Fagotti — 2 Corni in Fa — 2 Trombe in Fa — Timpani — Fagotto princ. — Violini — Viola — Violoncello Contrabasso

6

E. E. 6082

8

E.E. 6032

**10**

**14**

**18**

160

E. E. 6032

E. E. 6032

E.E. 6032

# II

# III

RONDÒ - Allegro

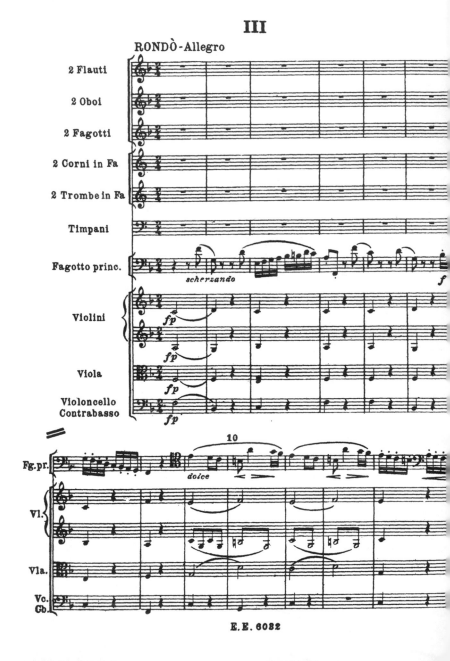

44

50